# Mermaid Poems

C     Bevan lives in a cobwebby house with her
      d, Martin, her son, Ben, a family of stick
i     s and a brown hamster called Malteser.
S     ed to be a teacher, but now she spends
      of her time writing poems. Her favourite
h     es are acting, wearing hats and riding
a     nd her village on a big purple tricycle.

L   a Jones lives in a tiny cottage by a misty hill
with her husband, Shaun. She likes painting
pict es, eating Marmite on toast and day-
dr  ming.

*Other books from Macmillan*

MORE FAIRY POEMS
By Clare Bevan
Illustrated by Lara Jones

BALLERINA POEMS
By Clare Bevan
Illustrated by Lara Jones

CRAZY MAYONNAISY MUM
Poems by Julia Donaldson
Illustrated by Nick Sharratt

# Mermaid Poems

By Clare Bevan

Illustrated by Lara Jones

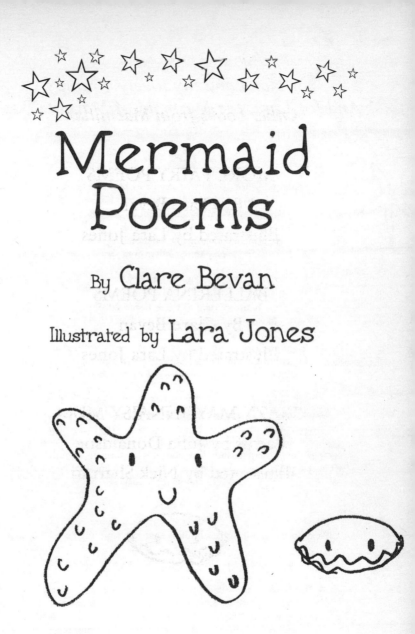

MACMILLAN CHILDREN'S BOOKS

*For Nana and my lovely Grampy.*
*And for Lara, the Mermaid of Marmite Bay.*
C.B.

First published 2005 by Macmillan Children's Books
an imprint of Macmillan Publishers Limited
20 New Wharf Road, London N1 9RR
Basingstoke and Oxford
Associated companies throughout the world
www.panmacmillan.com

ISBN 978-0-330-43785-1

Text copyright © Clare Bevan 2005
Illustrations copyright © Lara Jones 2005

The right of Clare Bevan and Lara Jones to be identified as the
author and illustrator of this book has been asserted by them in accordance
with the Copyright, Designs and Patents Act 1988.

5 7 9 8 6

A CIP catalogue record for this book is available from the British Library.

Printed and bound in the UK by CPI Mackays, Chatham ME5 8TD.

# Contents

# Shimmer, Glimmer

*You can sing this poem to the tune of "Twinkle, Twinkle, Little Star".*

Shimmer, glimmer, mermaid tails
With your gold and silver scales
How you sparkle, how you spin
While the little fishes grin.
Magic mermaids in the sea
Sing a sunny spell for me.

# Mermaid Names

*Clare saw this poem scratched in the sand.*

Mermaid names are not the same
As human names, my daughter.
Mermaid words are light as birds
That skim across the water . . .

Summer Tide, Silver Bride,
Swoop or Dart or Shimmer,
Ocean Girl or Seaweed Swirl,
Golden Scale or Glimmer,
Glass-of-Green or Rainbow Sheen,
Moonlight, Midnight Shiver,
Starry Trail, Nimble Tail,
Whirlpool, Wisp or Quiver . . .

Mermaid names are not the same
As ours, my human child,
Mermaid girls are rare as pearls,
And wonderful – and WILD!

# Marina the Mermaid

*Clare found this poem folded inside her swimming towel.*

Marina the mermaid
Lived under the sea
With a catfish, a dogfish
And sea horses (three.)

The dogfish, he guarded
Her mirror and comb.
The sea horses galloped
And pranced through the foam.

The catfish did nothing
But yawn on the sand
While she stroked his long whiskers
And fed him by hand.

Marina the mermaid
Swam east and swam west,
But that lazy old catfish,
She loved him the best.

# Stars of the Sea

*Clare read this little poem by starlight.*

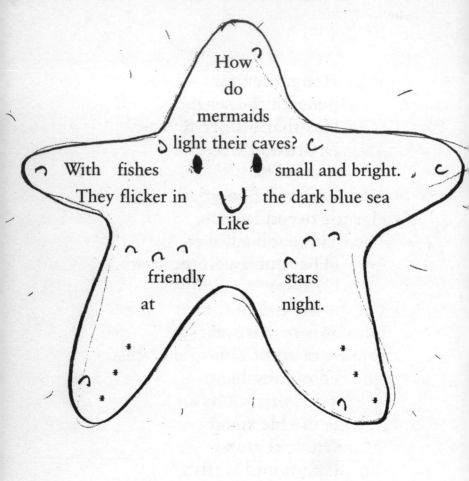

How
do
mermaids
light their caves?
With fishes small and bright.
They flicker in the dark blue sea
Like
friendly stars
at night.

# The Mermaid's Garden

*Clare discovered this poem underneath her
seaside spade.*

Her garden far
Beneath the seas
Has shark-tooth fences,
Driftwood trees,
A coral bed of
Crimson flowers,
Seaweed hedges,
Three tall towers
(That once were masts
Of ships, you know!),
A rocky bank
Where starfish glow,
A maze of blue anemones
(That tremble in
The salty breeze),
A marble statue
Old and grand
(She found it buried
In the sand),
A pathway made

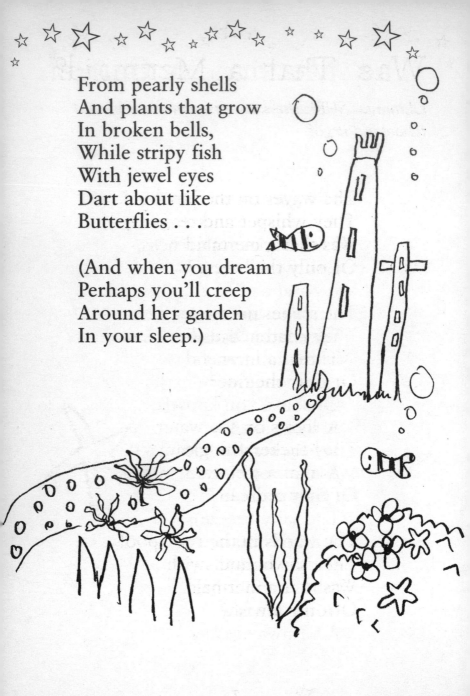

From pearly shells
And plants that grow
In broken bells,
While stripy fish
With jewel eyes
Dart about like
Butterflies . . .

(And when you dream
Perhaps you'll creep
Around her garden
In your sleep.)

# Was That a Mermaid?

*Clare was SURE she saw a mermaid once – but where did it go?*

The waves on the sandbank
They whisper and tease . . .
Was that a mermaid
Or only the breeze?

The stones on the seashore
They chatter and slide . . .
Was that a mermaid
Or only the tide?

The lights on the water
They flicker and gleam . . .
Was that a mermaid
Or only a dream?

The weeds in the rock pool
They shiver and swish . . .
Was that a mermaid
Or only a wish?

The songs in my seashell,
They echo and call . . .
Was that a mermaid
Or nothing at all?

# Mermaid School

*A crowd of little fishes is called a school. So what is a crowd of little mermaids called? Perhaps it is a SPLASH!*

What do mermaids learn at school?

How to sing beside a pool.
How to catch a flying fish.
How to grant an earth-child's wish.
How to chime a ship's old bell.
How to curl inside a shell.
How to win a sea-horse race.
How to swoop and dive and chase
Faster than the dolphin teams.
How to swim the silver beams
Of the small and misty moon.
How to play a magic tune.
How to tame a hungry shark.
How to find (when nights grow dark)
Hidden caves where treasures lie.
How to read a cloudy sky.
How to make a pearly ring.
How to mend a seabird's wing.
How to use a golden comb.

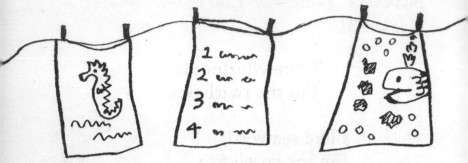

How to balance on the foam.
How to greet a friendly whale.
How to spin upon your tail.
How to twist and leap and turn . . .

This is what the mermaids learn.

# The Mermaid Rap

*Mermaids say this poem to the beat of a turtle's flipper.*

I like whirlpools,
I'm the twirliest.

I like seaweed,
I'm the swirliest.

I like moonlight,
I'm the sleepiest.

I like whale songs,
I'm the weepiest.

I like clownfish,
I'm the funniest.

I like blue skies,
I'm the sunniest.

I like sea caves,
I'm the gloomiest.

I like storm winds,
I'm the zoomiest.

I like lobsters,
I'm the snappiest.

I like seasides –
I'm the HAPPIEST!

# Shark Spell

*This poem reminds Clare of an old magpie rhyme.*

This is a spell the mermaids say
When scary sharks come out to play . . .

ONE    –    for storms, and
TWO    –    for danger.
THREE  –    a shipwreck.
FOUR   –    a stranger.
FIVE   –    a bracelet, floating down.
SIX    –    a rusty, royal crown.
SEVEN  –    a golden sunny day,

And . . .

EIGHT  –    it's time to swim away!

# Green and Blue

*This poem was pinned to Clare's sun hat with a very strange feather.*

The lovely tail
Of the new Mer-Queen
Is EVERY shade of
Blue and green . . .

The blue of seas,
Of sunny skies,
Of meadow flowers,
Of butterflies,
Of blackbird eggs,
Of velvet nights,
Of toy balloons,
Of party lights,
Of royal robes,
Of sapphire rings,
Of icebergs and
Of magpie wings.

The green of weeds,
Of lizard scales,
Of chestnut trees,
Of woodland trails,
Of lettuce leaves,
Of apple skins,
Of emeralds,
Of shiny fins,
Of summer lawns,
Of tiny flies,
Of hedges and
Of tom cat eyes,

The Mer-Queen's tail
(I tell you true)
Is EVERY shade of
Green and blue.

# The Spiral Stone

*Clare found this poem when she was searching the beach for fossils.*

The mermaid's door is shaped like a moon
With a tiny flap for her pet fishes.
Crystals twinkle on every window ledge,
And her walls are lined with wonders
From the coral forests
And the sea caves.

Her guard lobster sits
On a cushion of sea-moss
And counts each one . . .

There are thousands of shells,
Hundreds of jewels,
A cascade of glittering coins,
And no end of lost treasures –
A queen's necklace,
A pirate's sword,
A sailor's buckle,
A royal baby's first crown.

But strangest and best
Is the Spiral Stone
She found on a grey beach,
On a grey day.

It is heavy in her hand
And its coils are as tight
As a sea horse's tail.
Sometimes she touches its twists
And wonders if a sea wizard carved it
Long years ago,
Or if it fell from a spinning star
One quiet midnight.

When she sleeps,
She tucks it under her green pillow
And dreams of forgotten seas
Where monsters swim,
Where stones come to life,
And spiral shells dance
In the waters of time.

*(I think her Spiral Stone was a fossil, don't you?)*

# Letters in Bottles

*Clare once sent a message in a bottle – but she hasn't had an answer yet.*

In the Under-Sea Museum
(Below the deepest wave)
You'll find a THOUSAND bottles
In a sleepy, creepy cave,
And EACH ONE holds a letter
That was written long ago –
What happened to the writers?
I'm afraid we'll never know . . .

I'm stranded on an island.
There's no one else. Just me.
But PLEASE don't send a rescue ship –
I'm happy as can be.

Across the seas
This note has come.
I'm safe. I'm well.
Please tell my mum.

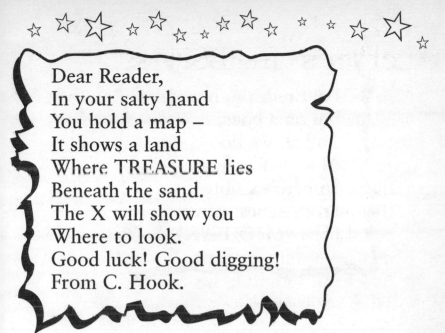

Dear Reader,
In your salty hand
You hold a map –
It shows a land
Where TREASURE lies
Beneath the sand.
The X will show you
Where to look.
Good luck! Good digging!
From C. Hook.

I'm tired. I'm bored.
I'm on a boat,
And all we do
ALL DAY is float.
So here's a note
From me to you.
(The year is 1892.)

You've found my letter!
Write back soon –
This morning or
This afternoon.
I'll wait. I'll watch
The stormy seas.
I'm VERY lonely.
Write back! Please!

# The Aquarium

*Clare went to this aquarium once. She didn't like it at all.*

"Roll up, now! Roll up!"
Called the man on the pier.
Come, visit the MERMAID!
Last chance this year."

I paid him my penny,
I tiptoed inside,
I thought he had tricked me,
I thought he had lied . . .

But there was the mermaid,
Alone in the pool,
Just like the pictures
I'd studied at school.

Her hair was as glossy
And golden and wet,
Her tail was as silver
As moonlight, and yet

Her song was the saddest
I ever had heard,
Her eyes were as dull
As a poor, captured bird.

I ran from the mermaid,
I ran from the pier,
But still, in my head,
It's her voice that I hear.

And still, in my dreams,
She is gazing at me
As I carry her gently
Back home to the sea.

# The Mer-Child

*Clare heard this story while she was buying a fishing net.*

Last week, I found a mer-child!
I caught her in my net.
I wrapped her in my beach towel
(Her hair was dripping wet).

I took her for a bus ride,
I took her home for tea –
She wouldn't eat her crumpets
(She gave them all to me).

Her chair was much too squashy
(She wanted stones and rocks),
The rugs were dry and itchy,
She laughed at shoes and socks.

She didn't like our bathroom,
The sink was far too tight,
The water wasn't salty
And the colour wasn't right.

I told her bedtime stories
But she didn't understand,
Her songs were sharp and squeaky
And she filled her bed with sand.

Last week, I found a mer-child,
Or maybe SHE found me –
I took her to the seashore
And there I set her free.

# The Fisher Lad

*Clare found this poem inside an old wooden boat.*

One stormy day, a fisher lad,
He tumbled from his boat,
And no one knows how far he fell
Or how he came to float.
"We know," sing the seagulls,
"We know," sing the shells,
"We know," sing the running waves,
But no one ever tells.

The fisher lad, he lives alone,
He wanders on the sand.
"I cannot say," he groans aloud,
"Who brought me safe to land."
"We know," sing the fishes,
"We know," sing the bells,
"I know," sings a mermaid voice,
But no one ever tells.

# Pretty Lottie Lee

*Lottie Lee is an old lady now. She told this tale to
Clare.*

"Mermaid! Little mermaid!"
Called pretty Lottie Lee.
"Bring my jolly sailor lad
Safe across the sea."
The mermaid smiled and she cast a spell
With her spiral stone and her singing shell –
"Let his sails be full,
Let his skies be clear,
Let his ship come home
In less than a year."

"Mermaid! Little mermaid!"
Called jolly Sailor Jack.
"Keep my pretty seaside girl
Safe till I come back."
The mermaid laughed and she cast a spell
With her golden comb and her silver bell –
"Let her cares be light
As a summer dress,
Let her dreams come true
In a year. Or less."

"Mermaid! Little mermaid!"
Called a sailor and his bride.
"May all your days be bright and blue,
Your seas be deep and wide."

# The Singing Shell

*Clare found a singing shell – but she left it on the beach.*

You say you saw a singing shell
And kept it for your own.
My foolish child – I think you've found
A mermaid's mobile phone!

If it makes a ting, tang, ting,
If you feel it jiggle,
If you catch the ripple of
A mermaid's teasy giggle,
If you hear a mermaid spell,
A mermaid song or two,
If a sleepy mermaid voice
Tells stories all night through,
If your shell begins to shake
And shiver in your hand . . .

Perhaps you'd better take it back
And leave it on the sand.

# The Mermaid in the Pond

*Clare found this poem on a lily pad.*

Did someone wave a magic wand?
I've seen a MERMAID in our pond!

She's not a newt or a tiny whale,
She's not a frog – I saw her tail.

She's not a fish or a dragonfly,
She waved at me and winked her eye.

She combed her glinty golden hair,
Then splashed away to who-knows-where . . .

And all she left for me, for me,
Was one white pebble from the sea.

# Birthday Mermaids

*Clare saw this poem underneath a rather sandy sandwich.*

Birthday mermaids
Like to eat
Toasted seaweed
(Not too sweet),
Bowls of frozen
Sea-foam, and
Sandwiches
(With proper sand).

Birthday mermaids
Like to play
Hunt-the-Flatfish,
Ride-the-ray,
Catch-the-swordfish
(By his nose),
Hide-and-seek
Where coral grows.

Birthday mermaids
Like to get
Mirrors or
A sea-horse pet,
Cuddly whales
That make a noise,
Bouncy sponges,
Driftwood toys.

Birthday mermaids
Like to shout,
Sing a song and
Twist about,
Make a wish
And then (no doubt)
Blow their sparkly
Starfish out!

# Mermaids' Purses

*Clare found this poem hidden inside a mermaid's purse.*

Silly fishes lay their eggs
Where greedy jaws can grind them.
But dogfish pop their eggs in pods
And kindly mermaids find them.

The mermaids hide the pods away
From hungry birds and beaks
Until the baby fishes hatch
(They wait for weeks and weeks).

The empty pods are washed ashore
To puzzle me and you.
We call them MERMAIDS' PURSES, and
That's NOT made up . . .
                    IT'S TRUE!

# The Mer-Queen's Wedding

*Clare found this poem inside a big pink conch shell.*

The Mer-Palace bells shook so hard
The whole sea seemed to ripple,
And all the little mer-children
Raced and chased along a silver path of
    moonlight
To a magic circle of sand.

Here the crowds waited:
The shrimps and the lobsters,
The patient limpets and the excited prawns,
The prancing sea horses and the fluttering
    rays,
While the old octopus took her place
In a shower of blue bubbles.

Then the great conch shells hooted,
Tan-ta-roooo! Tan-ta-roooo!
And at last the Mer-King swooped down
On his mighty golden swordfish.
"How handsome he looks,"

Called the whales.
"How magnificent in his crown of shells,"
Gurgled the turtles.
"Hush," cried the mermaids,
Swishing their jewelled tails.
"Here she comes! Here she is!"

And here she was,
The Mer-Queen bride.
Shy as an oyster,
Pretty as a rainbow,
Graceful as a summer cloud.

Gently, so gently,
The Mer-King placed a circle of pearls
On her sleek head.
Happily, so happily,
The Mer-Queen threaded a ribbon of stars
Through his long, green beard.

"Long life," sighed the old octopus,
Wiping her eyes with one shaky tentacle,
"And oceans of joy."

Then all the mer-people cheered and
    shouted,
"Long life! Oceans of Joy!"
Until the jellyfish danced their beautiful
    Wedding Ballet
And the party began.

# Sea Spells

*Clare found this poem inside her umbrella one wet seaside morning.*

Spells to stop the Mer-King frowning.
Spells to save a child from drowning.
Spells to mend a leaky boat.
Spells to help an iceberg float.
Spells to snatch a pirate's gold.
Spells to warm a heart that's cold.
Spells to hide the wandering whale
From the hunter. Spells to sail
Around the world and back again.
Spells to mix the sun and rain
Into rainbows. Spells to bind
Salt and water. Spells to find
Missing treasures. Spells to make
Storm clouds vanish. Spells to take
Sharks away from frightened fishes.
Spells to grant your dearest wishes.
Spells to let our sweet Mer-Queen
Skim and swim, yet NOT be seen
(Even when the skies are blue)
By ANYONE . . . except for YOU!

# Turtle Rider

*This poem was given to Clare by an ENORMOUS turtle.*

Who wants a turtle ride? Who wants a trip
On good King Neptune's shellback ship?

Glide to the north where the sunsets glow,
Glide to the south where the palm trees
    grow,
Glide to the east where the rivers flow,

Jump on your saddle! Away you float
On good King Neptune's shellback boat.

Glide to the west where the warm winds
    blow,
Glide to the sunshine or glide to the snow,
Glide on the currents wherever they go,

Now, turn your turtle. Tug on his rein
And proudly glide back home again.

Who wants a turtle ride?
Who wants a trip
On good King Neptune's
Shellback ship?

# The Cabin Boy

*Clare once saw the Cabin Boy, gazing out to sea.*

The fishermen cast their nets on the water
(Wind on the waves, wind on the sea)
And they captured the Mer-King's littlest
    daughter.
("Father, oh father!" wailed she.)

They gave her a shawl and a second-hand
    gown
(Wind on the waves, wind on the tide)
While the storm blew up and the rain beat
    down.
("Riches and rubies," they cried.)

The Cabin Boy watched while the stars lit
    the skies
(Wind on the waves, wind on the sea)
And he saw the tears in her sorrowful eyes.
("No one shall hurt her," said he.)

He lifted her up and he let her swim free
(Wind on the waves, wind on the tide)
And he waved farewell to the girl from the
    sea.
("She vanished like snowflakes," he lied.)

The Mer-King's daughter, she murmured a
    charm
(Wind on the waves, wind on the sea)
"Oh, let him be sheltered from heartache
    and harm."
("But I still love my mermaid," sighed he.)

# Madame de la Mare's Ballet School

*Clare found this poem curled through a little silver ring.*

Madame de la Mare
Balances on the very tip
Of her pale pink tail,
Peers over her pale pink spectacles
And waits for silence.

The little mermaids point their fins.
They try SO hard
Not to wobble
As the music begins,
And Madame beats time
With her sea-urchin spike.

"First position!" she calls.
Ten tails flick left.
"Second." They flick to the right.
"Third." A whirl.
"Fourth." A swirl.
"Fifth." A flutter of the fingers.
"And sixth." Most difficult of all.

A corkscrew spin, up, up,
Into the starlight
With wide-open eyes
And not even the smallest splutter
Or splash.

Now the little mermaids tumble
Dizzily down
In a giggling whirlpool
And flap their tails
On the sandy floor.

Madame de la Mare claps her hands
To make her silver rings jingle.
"Bravo," she cries.
"Well spun, my children."
And she rewards her clumsy ballerinas
With a rare and glittering smile.

# Nobody Smiled

*Clare found this poem underneath her sandy sandwiches.*

Nobody smiled below the great grey sea.

The catfish would not purr.
The dogfish would not wag his tail.
The clownfish could not think of a single
    seabed joke.
Even the little mermaid
Forgot how to sing.

"The Mer-Queen has vanished,"
Murmured the green weeds.
"No one has seen her for days and days,"
Called the dolphins.
"Perhaps she is ill,"
Wailed the young sardines.
"Perhaps she is lost,"
Rasped the old sea slug.

Then the big castle bell
(That had once fallen from a golden ship)
Began to clang
Once, twice, three times,
While the sea turned a brilliant blue.

Ripples of surprise stroked the catfish
And made him purr.
Ripples of happiness patted the dogfish
And made him wag his tail.
Ripples of laughter tickled the clownfish
And made him blow bubbles.
Ripples of music reached the mermaid's cave
And made her sing.

"The Mer-Queen is home!
Hooray! Hooray!
And a little Mer-Princess
Was born today!"

# The Sea-Pony Club

*Clare found this poem inside a tiny blue riding helmet.*

Ten tiny mermaids on ten tiny horses
Canter in circles round coral-reef courses . . .

Over the prickly
Tickly jumps
(One or two tumbles,
Three or four bumps),
Trek through a tangle
Of thick, weedy hedges
(Look out for lobsters
On wobbly ledges),
Smile at the octopus
Guarding her cave,
Swoop with the current
And splash with the wave,
Dive past the sea slugs
Who snooze on the wall,
Leap over limpets
And try not to fall . . .

Here comes the finish – who's lost? And
     who's won?
Nobody's noticed. They're all having FUN!

# The Rainbow

*Clare saw this poem in the sky, one showery
seaside day.*

The flying fishes dived around
Their lovely Mermaid Queen.
They said, "She has the sweetest face
Our water world has seen".
"She has the sweetest temper,
The sweetest songs," they said.
And they flew a salty rainbow
All above the Mer-Queen's head.

# The Four Mermaids

*This poem was written in sea water on a big flat stone. Clare had to copy it VERY quickly, before it faded away.*

The Mermaid of Autumn
Sings, "Frost on the breeze."

The Mermaid of Winter
Sings, "Shiver and sneeze."

The Mermaid of Springtime
Sings, "Drizzle and spray."

The Mermaid of Summer
Sings, "Sunshine! Hooray!"

# The Mermaid of Zennor

*Clare heard this old story in a Cornish teashop beside the sea.*

Oh, the folk in Zennor churchyard
And the folk in Zennor town,
They all were turned to statues
As the sun went down.

And they could not move till morning
And they could not speak till day
Of the mermaid who came singing
And the lad she stole away.

Then the women lit their candles
And the sailors shone a light
In case the pair came swimming
Safely home one Sunday night.

But the storyteller wonders,
Oh, the storyteller wishes
That the lad will live forever
With the mermaid. And the fishes.

(Nobody knows if the story is true – but
there IS a carving of a mermaid inside the
church at Zennor!)

# The Little Mermaid's Story

## 1. What the Little Mermaid Said

*This poem tells you why the Little Mermaid wanted to lose her fishy tail.*

On a glittering boat,
On a glittering sea,
I first saw my prince
(Though he didn't see me).

On a terrible night,
In a terrible storm,
I rescued my prince
And my breath kept him warm.

On a blustery beach,
On a blustery day,
A little earth-princess,
She led him away.

By the bright morning star,
By the cool morning dew,
I wish I could skip
Like an earth-princess too.

# 2. What the Old Octopus Said

*This poem tells you how the Little Mermaid found the Sea-Witch.*

In a sea cave dark and dangly,
Where the weeds hang green and tangly,
    Lives a witch
           With snaky hair.

Here she shakes her bells so jangly,
Casts her spells so loud and spangly,
    You can find her
           IF YOU DARE!

# 3. What the Friendly Fishes Said

*Now the Little Mermaid's friends try to warn her about the Sea-Witch.*

Mermaid, do not trust the witch
To charm your prince or make you rich.

Do not trust her ripply spells
Or all the tempting tales she tells.

Do not trust her twinkling eyes –
Clever minds may not be wise.

Do not trust her when she sings
Of stony castles, kindly kings.

Do not laugh. Do not rejoice,
Or she will swap your pretty voice

For lonely tears and years of pain . . .
And you will never sing again.

# 4. What the Sea-Witch Said

*Oh dear, I'm afraid the Little Mermaid didn't
listen to her friends.*

This is the spell that the Sea-Witch spoke –
Shout it aloud with a clap and a croak . . .

ONE GIFT
YOU CHOSE –
TWO FEET,
TEN TOES,
WISH HARD,
EYES CLOSE,
SNIP, SNAP,
TAIL GOES,
LEGS GROW,
KEEP THOSE.

NOW HEAR
MY CHOICE –
I'LL TAKE
YOUR VOICE.

This is the spell that the mermaid heard –
Tiptoe away, without one word . . .

# 5. What the Seagulls Said

*The Little Mermaid cannot speak, but she CAN
dance – all the way to her prince's palace.*

Now the Little Mermaid woke in a strange
   world
Where her mouth made no sound,
And even her laughter
Was as silent as smoke.

Her two new legs
With their pointy feet
And ten wriggly toes
Should have made her giggle and sing,
But instead she could only spin
And skip
Across the shivery ribbon of sand.

Each tiny step bruised her tender skin,
Yet still she told herself,
"I am happy,
So happy."
And when she felt the first tickle
Of wet grass on her soft heels,
When she stood on tiptoe
Below the palace walls,
When she saw her prince
In his silver robes
Like a star against the misty sky,
She danced for joy.

Then the young prince gazed down
And smiled,
While a girl as fragile as a gull's feather
Twirled
Among a sea of blue flowers.

## 6. What the Prince Said

*The prince did not ask the Little Mermaid to marry him – but he loved her quietness and the magical way she danced.*

Oh, call for the girl
Whose steps are so light,
Whose smile is so sad,
Whose tears are so bright –

She shall dance for my bride
At our wedding,
      TONIGHT!

# 7. What the Earth-Princess Said

*So, the prince married the earth-princess who had found him on the sand. And the Little Mermaid danced for them until her poor heart broke.*

At the wedding ball,
At the wedding ball,
Who is the sweetest,
The fleetest of all?
And who is the girl
With the flickering feet,
Who whirls in a circle
So perfect and neat?

Some say a wind and the waves must have
    brought her,
The girl who can dance like a fish in the
    water.

On the palace lawn,
On the palace lawn,
Who is as swift
As a swallow at dawn?
And who is the girl
Who can spin on a pin?
And where did she come from?
And who let her in?

Some say a magical net must have caught her,
The girl who can dance like a fish in the
    water.

At the end of day,
At the end of day,
Who is as silent
As moonshine in May?
And where is the girl
Who was weeping alone?
And why is she sleeping
As still as a stone?

Some say she once was a sea-wizard's
    daughter,
The girl who can dance like a fish in the
    water.

(Don't worry – she didn't die . . .)

# 8. What the Spirits of the Air Said

*The Little Mermaid was not dead. Her beautiful spirit was carried into the sky, where she could fly above the world and keep watch over the prince and his princess for as long as they lived.*

Little Mermaid,
Don't despair,
Pin the starlight
In your hair,
Join the spirits
Of the air.

Float away from
Hurt and pain,
Leap the clouds
And ride the rain,
Dive and dart
And live again.

When the shadows
Drift away,
Watch the silver
Fishes play,
Guard your prince
By night. By day.

Little Mermaid
Wave goodbye,
Let your sorrows
Fade and fly –
Join the spirits
Of the sky.

(And I truly believe she lived happily ever
after.)

# The Little Mermaid's Statue

*Clare found this poem hidden behind the little statue.*

Have you seen the little statue
Who gazes out to sea,
Dreaming of the human world
Where once she longed to be?

Dreaming of the salty waves
Where once she used to play,
Dreaming of the prince she loved
When once he sailed away.

Dreaming of the magic cave
Where wishes once came true,
Dreaming of the dancing feet
That once were light and new.

Dreaming of the hopes she had
That once shone bright as gold,
Dreaming of the stormy tears
That once fell fast and cold.

Dreaming of the spirit land
Where once she fluttered free . . .
The lonely little statue
Who gazes out to sea.


(There is a statue of the Little Mermaid,
but it is far away in a land called Denmark.
If you are lucky, perhaps YOU will see it
one day.)

# She Sells Seashells

*Clare says that only the SMALLEST mermaids can live inside seashells.*

She sells seashells
On the seabed . . .

"Mermaid houses!
Pink, blue, red!
Tiny doors to
Let you in.
Twisty stairs that
Steeply spin.
Little flaps to
Let fish out.
Pebble chairs that
Rock about.

Sponges (soft) for
Dreamy sleep.
Windows where the
Starfish peep.
Coral tables.
Pearly plates.

Sandy gardens.
Driftwood gates.

Mermaid houses!
Pink, red, blue!"

She sells seashells
Just for YOU.

# A Mer-Puzzle

*Mermaids like to play puzzle games on long
winter evenings.*

My first is in OCEAN – but not in DEEP,
My second's in SEA HORSE – but not in
    LEAP,
My third is in MERMAID – but not in
    TAIL,
My fourth is in SPARKLE – and also in
    SCALE,
My last is in GLOOMY – but not in
    CAVES,
My whole is a wonder beneath the waves.

I'm the CORAL in the sea.
Did you find the hidden ME?
ANSWER:

69

# The Mermaid's Granny

*Clare found this poem curled inside a glass bottle.*

Oh, swim through time with me, with me,
And we shall see what we shall see . . .

The mermaid's granny is a girl
As frisky as the winds that swirl,

Her trailing hair is seaweed green,
Her face is lovely as a queen,

Her little hands have silver nails,
She catches fishes by their tails

And murmurs words both old and strange
Until their scales begin to change

To coins of gold! She sets them free –
The glinting treasures of the sea,

Then flicks her tail and nimbly slips
Between the wooden sailing ships,

And with a laugh she dives away
To vanish in the mists of day.

Oh, swim through time with me, with me,
And we shall see what we shall see . . .

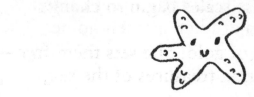

# The Mermaid of the Coral

*A little fish sang this song to Clare in a summer dream.*

The Mermaid of the Coral,
Her hair was sunset red,
She knew the hidden places
Where the little fishes fed.

She stroked their fins with fingers
That were lighter than a fly,
She taught them how to trust her
As the years went whirling by.

The Mermaid of the Coral,
Her hair grew white as foam,
And all the little fishes came
To guard her seashell home.

# Mermaid Questions

*Clare heard this poem on a lonely, stony beach.*

Mermaid, do you ever miss
The blackbirds in the sky?
Oh no! I have the singing whales
Who greet me with their cry.

Mermaid, do you ever miss
The daisy and the rose?
Oh no! I have a garden where
The flowery coral grows.

Mermaid, do you ever miss
The butterflies and bees?
Oh no! I have the rainbow fish
Who flutter through the seas.

Mermaid, do you ever miss
The gleaming city lights?
Oh no! I have my own bright star
To shine on lonely nights.

# Poor Mr Octopus

*This poem was given to Clare by a rather confused octopus.*

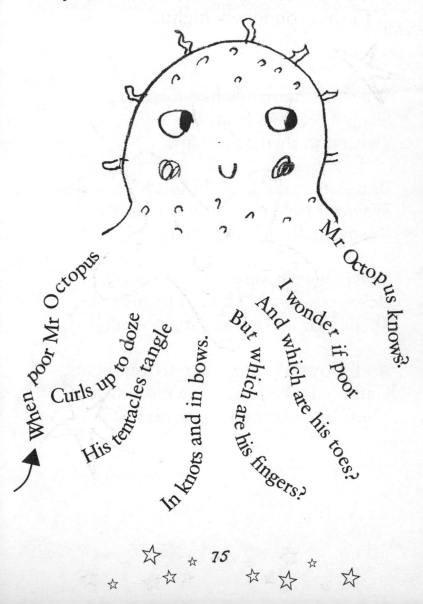

When poor Mr Octopus

Curls up to doze

His tentacles tangle

In knots and in bows.

But which are his fingers?

And which are his toes?

I wonder if poor

Mr Octopus knows?

# What Do Mermaids Like to Wear?

*Clare found this poem neatly tied with a ribbon of seaweed.*

What do mermaids like to wear?
Seagull feathers from the air
Twisted in their salty hair,

Bracelets made from bright blue scales,
Seaweed ribbons for their tails,
Wispy, drifty summer veils,

Glassy jewels, smooth and round,
Royal treasures (lost and found),
Shells that make a singing sound,

And snowflake stars like frozen lights,
Gathered when the ice-wind bites –
These are worn on party nights.

# Mermaid Adverts

*Helpful limpets stuck these adverts to the rocks near Clare's deckchair.*

Stars for your tailfins,
Silver and sparkly!
(Gleam in the sea when
The storm clouds loom darkly.)

Magical combs,
Gold, green and white.
(Won't pull your hair
When the tangles are tight.)

Saddles for sea horses,
Feathery light.
(Say if you sit on
The left or the right.)

Buy your looking glass from US.
We make lovely shiny ones . . .
Round and square and big and small
And really, really tiny ones.

Sea horses! Sea horses!
Frisky and fast,
Ready for racing –
Buy while stocks last.

Super-soft sponges –
Cosy for snoozing,
Squashy for bouncing,
Lots of fun choosing.

Flying lessons!
Come and try –
All our fishes
Flutter high.
Jump aboard
And touch that sky!

# Hush! Hush!

*This poem was hiding under Clare's beach sandals.*

The seaside stones say, "Hush! Hush!"
The busy fish say, "Rush! Rush!"

The secret caves say, "Hide! Hide!"
The sea-horse teams say, "Ride! Ride!"

The rusty bells say, "Ring! Ring!"
The lonely whales say, "Sing! Sing!"

The swooping birds say, "Fly! Fly!"
The hollow shells say, "Why? Why?"

The frisky winds say, "Blow! Blow!"
The sailing ships say, "Go! Go!"

The grumpy crabs say, "Snap! Snap!"
The greedy gulls say, "Flap! Flap!"

The summer skies say, "Sun! Sun!"
The Mer-Princess says, "Fun! Fun!"

# Mermaid Facts

*These facts were sent to Clare by sea-mail.*

1. The Mer-King's beard really IS green, and it would reach to the bed of the sea if it wasn't twisted into neat knots.

2. The Mer-Queen's favourite hobbies are exploring shipwrecks and learning new languages. She can speak Octopus, Limpet, Shark and Lobster. She also knows a few easy whale songs.

3. The Sea-Witch's favourite pets are two Starfish, called Silence and Solitude.

4. The most popular names for mermaids this year are Silver-fin and Dazzle.

5. The most popular names for mer-boys this year are Dart and Wave-whistler.

6. The most popular under-sea sports are sea-horse riding and fish flying. Seashell helmets MUST be worn, but gull-feather gloves are just for fun.

7. The favourite party present is a pufferfish balloon. (The pufferfish enjoys it too.)

8. The BEST party lights (especially when it's dark) are luminous jellyfish, because they like to bob about when the music is playing.

9. The MOST important mermaid rule is never forget where you put your comb and mirror.

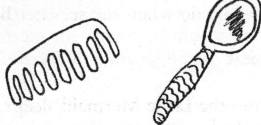

10. A mermaid's MOST precious possession is the magic pearl she is given on her first birthday.

# Mermaid Jokes

*Clare says she borrowed these jokes from a funny clownfish.*

What does the Little Mermaid call her pet turtle?
*Shelly.*

What does the Little Mermaid call her pet swordfish?
*Spike.*

What does the Little Mermaid do when she sees her friends?
*Wave.*

What does she do when she sees her BEST friend?
*A BIG wave.*

Where does the Little Mermaid sleep?
*On the seabed.*

What sort of fish goes wibble, wobble?
*A jellyfish.*

What sort of fish likes icebergs?
*A skate.*

What sort of shellfish is VERY strong?
*A mussel.*

What sort of sea creature has SHOCKING manners?
*An electric eel.*

What sort of fish has PERFECT manners?
*An angelfish.*

What sort of sea creature is a BIG softy?
*A sponge.*

AND . . .

What sort of ship is frightened of the Little Mermaid?
*A nervous wreck!*

(Did you guess them all? Do you know any more?
Are you EVEN FUNNIER than the clown-fish?)

# If You See the Mermaid Queen

*Clare caught this poem as it fluttered across the beach.*

If you see the Mermaid Queen
Don't tell. Don't tell.

Do not mark her hiding place
With stone. Or shell.

Do not sing her magic tune
In school. In town.

Do not draw her looking glass.
Her comb. Her crown.

Do not speak her secret name
At home. At play.

If you see the Mermaid Queen
Don't say. Don't say.

(Perhaps she'll grant your dearest wish
Some day. Some day.)

# A Seaside Puzzle

*Clare says she learned this puzzle at a mermaid's birthday party.*

Jiggle, joggle, bibble, bubble,
Everybody thinks we're trouble.
Lazily we lurk around,
Looping loops without a sound.
You say we are scary things,
Floaty fish with nasty stings.
I say we are twirly teams,
Sea umbrellas, summer dreams,
Hovering where moonlight gleams.

Who am I?

ANSWER:
Wibble, wobble on a dish –
I'm a jolly JELLYFISH!

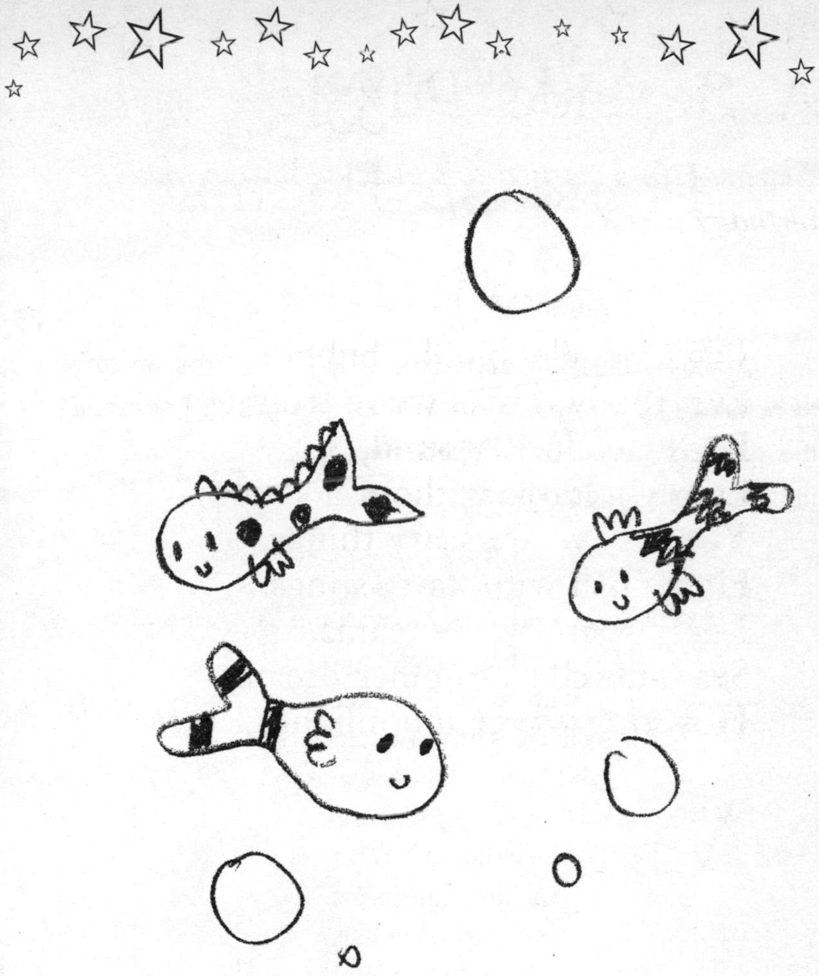

# CLARE BEVAN

# Princess Poems

Could you be a princess?

A gorgeous collection of poems filled with tips on how
to behave like a princess, meet the right prince and avoid
the dangers posed by wicked stepmothers, dragons and
unhappy fairy godmothers.

### If You Were a Princess

If YOU were a princess, what would YOU ride?
A small, metal dragon
with cogwheels inside?
A horse with white feathers
and hooves of black glass?
A silvery unicorn
pounding the grass?
A fluttering carpet
that chases the bats?
A big, golden pumpkin
With coachmen like rats?
A castle that sways
on an elephant's back?
A long, steamy train
Going clickety clack?
Or a ship with blue sails
And YOUR name on the side?
If YOU were a princess, what would YOU ride?

# A selected list of titles available from Macmillan Children's Books

The prices shown below are correct at the time of going to press. However, Macmillan Publishers reserves the right to show new retail prices on covers, which may differ from those previously advertised.

All Pan Macmillan titles can be ordered from our website, www.panmacmillan.com, or from your local bookshop and are also available by post from:

**Bookpost, PO Box 29, Douglas, Isle of Man IM99 1BQ**
Credit cards accepted. For details:
Telephone: 01624 677237
Fax: 01624 670923
Email: bookshop@enterprise.net
www.bookpost.co.uk

**Free postage and packing in the United Kingdom**